The Monster That Ate 3B

A play for schools and youth groups

Randall Lewton

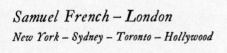
Samuel French – London
New York – Sydney – Toronto – Hollywood

ISBN 0 573 05084 8

Please see page viii for further copyright information

THE MONSTER THAT ATE 3B

The play was first performed at Calday Grange Grammar School, West Kirby with the following cast:

Frankie	Robert Denny
Tommy	Geraint Waters
George	Richard Chapman
Terry	James Stewart
Sean	Simon Kearsley
Richie	Silas Edmonds
Otto	Stephen Powell
Billy	Stephen McMillan
Fletch	Carne Simpson
John	Peter Kelly
Olly	Michael Green
Fordy	Daniel Roberts
Jimmy	Martin Hart
Cyril	Graham Davies
Mr Heywood	Keith Hill
Headmaster	Jim Corrigan
Luigi	Spencer Wakelam
Eduardo	Paul Humphreys
Dario	Robert Smith
Mayor	Daniel Meigh
Giuseppe	Grant Irlam
Carlo	Christopher Wimpenny
Carla	Alison Corran
Priest	Peter Griffiths
Policeman	Christopher McIver
Townspeople	Daniel Inman
	Marc Stephens
	Christopher Townsend
	Niall Mendes Da Costa
	Nicholas Lee
	Sally Granger
	Stuart Smith

and

iv

William Foster	Mark Williams
David Kimmer	Andrew Creer
Damon Roberts	David Croucher
Andrew Griffin	Pat Flanagan
Geoffrey Gotts	Anna Corbett
Edward Clarke	Simon Wood
James Cassie	Kevin Joshua
Richard Elston	Nevil Owen
Chris Penn	Stephen Bower
Patrick Hinton	Simon Fielding
Paul Bolton	Ian Thomson
Piers Williamson	Julian Moss
James Holland	James Foggin
Ralph Kesteven	Christopher Frost
Graham Potts	Christopher Home
Matthew Roche	

SYNOPSIS OF SCENES

ACT I	SCENE 1	Pericolo di Morte, Italy. The beach
	SCENE 2	England. A classroom
	SCENE 3	A coach
	SCENE 4	A Cross-Channel ferry
	SCENE 5	A train
	SCENE 6	Pericolo di Morte. The town square
	SCENE 7	The beach
	SCENE 8	The beach at night
ACT II	SCENE 1	The beach at dawn
	SCENE 2	The town
	SCENE 3	A rock at sea
	SCENE 4	The town square
	SCENE 5	The beach

CHARACTERS

An Italian Boy
Mr Heywood, a teacher
Headmaster
Sean
Tommy
Billy
Richie
Jimmy
Fletch
Sammy
John } pupils in 3B
George
Olly
Frankie
Otto
Terry
Cyril
Fordy
Mayor of Pericolo di Morte
Italian Woman
1st Italian Man
2nd Italian Man
3rd Italian Man
Carlo } the Goldonis
Carla } hotel owners
Giuseppe
Italian Boy
A Priest
Eduardo
Dario
Luigi
Policeman
Beach Cleaner
Fisherman
Italian Youth
Other members of 3B
Italian villagers
Italian boys

See Production Notes for details of how play can be
adapted to provide more female roles if required

PRODUCTION NOTES

The cast

The play was designed to allow a very large cast to all make a significant contribution to the final production. We had about seventy people. There is room for more but you could present the play very successfully with many fewer. Our cast consisted of two groups of "mimers" who handled all the mimed sections between them and the speaking parts were taken by a third group who did not take part in the mimes at all. Again, other arrangements are possible. The list of characters shows many more male than female roles in the play. If a more even balance is desired then it is quite possible for any of the following roles to become female with only a few minor changes necessary to the text:

Sean	Jimmy
Richie	Cyril
Billy	The boy in Scene 6
Fordy	Giuseppe
The Headmaster	Many of the "mimers"

The mimes

Although there are indications in the text of the content of the mimes they are only intended as suggestions or starting points. The play was designed to allow pupils to use the improvisational skills they practised in drama lessons and producers should try to employ as many of the actors' own ideas as possible.

Music

Whether you decide to use live or recorded music to accompany the mimes is up to you. Remember that permission must be sought to use recordings at public performances. Music with an Italian flavour is recommended in most cases. We used a lot of Verdi but please yourself.

Set

This can be as elaborate or as simple as you wish. You might like to create the town square as a basic set and play the other scenes using only furniture to create the classroom, bus, train etc. For the beach scenes you must have some "sea" in which the actors can swim and from which the monster can appear. We placed strips of blue cloth over a recessed area of the stage.

Swimmers and the monster could emerge between the strips. We rejected the idea of presenting the whole play in the school swimming pool. It is quite possible to perform the play in the round using little or no scenery at all.

The monster

It is worth spending some time and money on the monster and don't be tempted to let it be seen in Scenes 1 and 8. Save it. In constructing it you can aim for either horror or humour. I suggest the latter. Our monster resembled the usual idea of the Loch Ness monster and consisted of a metal framework for its head (with functional mouth) covered in green material. The framework rested on the shoulders of the operator, the green material being formed into a neck-like tube which went down to his feet which were below "water" level.

ACT I

Pericolo di Morte, Italy. The beach. Night

Music. There is a full moon. We can hear the sea. On a rock a boy is fishing.
He begins to sing to the tune of "O Sole Mio"

Italian Boy
　　　　　　　　　　Giuseppe Verdi
　　　　　　　　　　Inter-Milan
　　　　　　　　　　La Dolce Vita
　　　　　　　　　　Sophia Loren
　　　　　　　　　　Ferrari
　　　　　　　　　　Simpatico
　　　　　　　　　　Così Fan Tutte
　　　　　　　　　　Marco Polo

At this point a disgruntled stagehand plods on to the stage and dumps down
a large sign reading "ITALY". He glares at the audience and stomps off

The Italian Boy sings on

　　　　　　　　　　Antonioni
　　　　　　　　　　Venezia
　　　　　　　　　　Ciao Ciao Bambina
　　　　　　　　　　Autostrada
　　　　　　　　　　Spaghetti
　　　　　　　　　　Bolognese
　　　　　　　　　　Martini Secco
　　　　　　　　　　Campanile

A cloud crosses the moon. Darkness. Sinister music

　　　　　　　　　　Michelangelo
　　　　　　　　　　Antipasti
　　　　　　　　　　Arrivederci
　　　　　　　　　　Mussolini
　　　　　　　　　　Juventus
　　　　　　　　　　Boccaccio
　　　　　　　　　　Camparisoda
　　　　　　　　　　Pirandello

During this last verse the boy is attacked by the (invisible) sea-monster. Very
loud horrifying noises, screams. The light returns. Only the fishing rod
remains. The "ITALY" sign has a huge bite taken out of it

SCENE 2

England. A classroom

A bell rings

A class enters followed by Mr Heywood

Heywood All right. All right. Sit down. Shut up. Let's get this over with as quickly as possible. I've got better things to do even if you haven't. Come on. Come on.

Silence falls. He counts them

Thirty-two. Correct. Look at you. Young ambassadors is what the Headmaster calls you. Not what I'd call you. We should be keeping you lot well out of sight of our European partners if you ask me. One look at you, O'Casey, should be enough to demolish any last vestiges of confidence in Britain as a great industrial nation that might linger in the more remote corners of the continent. Wouldn't you say so, boy?

Sean What's a vestige, sir?

Tommy It's like a prisoner. You hold them to ransom.

Heywood Is Italy ready for you, Middleton? That's what I ask myself. And where will we hide *you*, Rowley, if we do not wish to set back the Channel tunnel project a hundred years? The Headmaster doesn't think of the effect on the European Economic Community when he arranges these jaunts. Relations are bad enough as it is. What's that noise?

He looks around the class. George is wearing personal stereo from which a drumbeat can be heard. Heywood marches over to him. George is unaware. Heywood lifts off the headphones. Suddenly very loud heavy metal music fills the air. Heywood drops the headphones back on. George turns it off and removes the headphones

What is that row, Etherege?

George "Stuff You", sir.

Heywood (*grabbing him by the lapels*) What!?

George It's a group, sir. "Stuff You", sir. It's their name.

Others back George up

Heywood Why are we here, Etherege?

George Oh, wow, well, I mean it's all part of the kind of pattern of the universe, sort of cosmic, isn't it?

Heywood No, Etherege. No. Why are we *here*? In Room two-one-two. At eleven o'clock today. I'll tell you. To arrange the final details of this trip. You are to listen to me, not ... not ... (*He gestures at the stereo*)

George (*helpfully*) "Stuff You", sir.

Heywood Watch it, Etherege. Just watch it! Sending you to the EEC could be its death blow. We must be grateful to the EEC. What's the EEC, Sheridan?

Richie Is it like O levels, sir?

Heywood The Common Market, Sheridan, we must be grateful to the Common Market and the Italian Ministry of Education who, in the interests of mutual understanding, have organized and for the most part financed our trip. What devious means the Headmaster used to persuade the powers that be to choose our school for this cultural exchange I cannot imagine.

Tommy We won the competition, sir.

Heywood Oh yes, that's right, Middleton, you won the competition. That will certainly go down as one of the school's great achievements of nineteen eighty-six, won't it? What a display of skill! "Guess how much spaghetti it would take to fill the leaning tower of Pisa"!

Tommy It wasn't a guess, sir. We calculated it.

Heywood Don't be so ... Otway, what are you doing?

Otto is gripping a desk at the sides and squeezing it. He and it shake with the tension

Are you all right? Good heavens, I think he's having a fit! O'Casey, go and fetch——

Otto (*relaxing*) It's all right, sir. I'm OK.

Richie He does it all the time.

Heywood Well have you seen a doctor about it?

Otto I'm not ill. It's part of me training programme.

Richie He does bodybuilding, sir.

Otto That one's supposed to develop me biceps.

Heywood Stand up, Otway. Out here.

Otto does so. He is rather small. Heywood walks around him

And how long have you been doing this bodybuilding?

Otto Six months, sir.

Heywood I have bad news for you, Otway. It isn't working.

Otto It is, sir. You should see me pectorals.

Heywood A generous offer which I will decline, Otway. Perhaps if you concentrated on your *mental* development it would be more use.

Otto But "the essence of education is the education of the body". Guess who said that, sir?

Heywood Roland Rat?

Otto Disraeli, sir. A strong body can be very useful.

Heywood Listen, Otway! When I am talking, you LISTEN! And leave your pectorals alone! Now. You all know that in order to be eligible for this trip, all the paperwork had to be completed by today. No excuses. If you haven't produced the documentation, you don't go. Where's my list? Here we are. First: the parental consent form.

The class in unison hold up forms in their left hands

(*Surprised*) Oh very good. Congratulations. Everybody. Collect those in please, Webster. Next: E111 medical form.

They all hold these up in their right hands. This happens with all the following

Everyone. Good. Very good. Collect those, Pinter. Right now this is
where some of you will have slipped up. Photograph for identity card . . . I
don't believe it. Otway, bring me those, would you?

The class are laughing at each other's pictures

All right. All right. Haven't finished yet. Certificate of innoculation
against typhoid. Rattigan. Certificate for yellow fever. Bridie. Cholera.
Beaumont. Malaria. Fletcher. Insurance form. Beckett.

Sean is writing in a notebook

Billy What's that?
Sean It's my journal. I'm going to keep a diary of the trip.
Billy But we're still in school. What are you writing?
Sean It's going to be a complete record. From start to finish. Everything I
see and hear. All the people I meet. Everything I do.
Fletch Am I going to be in it?
Sean You already are. Listen. (*He reads*) "Most of us have never been
abroad before. Fletch went to Pwllheli once and claims he could not
understand what the inhabitants were saying but this does not count. Mr
Heywood is already showing signs of stress. With any luck he will have a
nervous breakdown before we get back."

*By this time the classroom is in chaos with the collectors bumping into each
other, paper flying everywhere*

Heywood Is there anyone who has not handed in any one of those
documents?

The Headmaster enters

The pupils stand up

Head Sit down, please. Everything all right, Mr Heywood? Thought I'd
pop in and give you a hand with the paperwork.
Heywood Well, I think I have that all under control, Headmaster.

Papers are still flying everywhere

Head Good show. All looking forward to the trip, are we?
Pupils Yes, sir.
Head I certainly am. Italy! What a country. What does Italy mean to you?
Anybody. What does Italy mean to you?

Hands go up. He points to a few people

Sean Pizza, sir.
Billy Inter-Milan, sir.
Fletch Topless women, sir.
Head (*forgetting himself*) Oh, do you think there will be? No, no, no. You
are all clearly woefully ignorant of the country we are about to visit. Italy!
Italy is one of the cradles of European culture, a vast historical treasure-
house filled with a priceless store of architectural and artistic masterpieces

unparalleled in any country in the world. And as for pizza, boy, what do you know about pizza? The pizza they sell in this country is an insult to the great tradition of Italian cuisine. A true pizza has to be baked on the floor of an old brick oven after sweeping out the ashes of the fire. The oregano, the tomatoes and the anchovy fillets have to be blended in exactly the right proportions with the mozzarella. What's mozzarella? You!

Tommy There's nothing mozzarella with me, sir.

Head Don't be funny. Don't be funny. It's a cheese. Italian cheeses are superb. Bel Paese, gorgonzola, parmigiano, provatura, fontina, provolone. The Italians really know about food. I remember the first time I went to Italy, a little restaurant just off the Via Veneto. They served a saltimbocca (that's escalopes of veal rolled in sage leaves browned in butter and simmered in Marsala). Exquisite. I used to follow that with Monte Bianco, which is a chestnut purée flavoured with sugar and rum and piled high with whipped cream. Heaven! And ... and ... the wine ...

> "O for a draught of vintage that hath been
> Cool'd a long age in the deep-delved earth
> O, for a beaker full of the warm South
> Full of the true, the blushful Hippocrene ..."

Heywood hands him a mug of coffee

A Campari appetiser followed by a Riserva Chianti and——

Italian romantic music fades in as the Lights go down except for a pink spot on the Headmaster

—and then an Asti or Canelli (made from the moscato bianco, the muscat grape, very sweet) and with the coffee a liqueur, perhaps Strega or Sambuca. I can almost taste them still, after thirty years. Ah yes, it was at that restaurant that I first saw Gina.

Heavenly choir

Oh the beauties of Italy! Warm, soft, brown skin, jet-black hair with the sheen of silk and eyes, dark deep pools.

Tommy And that's only the fellers.

Head Oh so soft, so delicate, such sparkle, amusing but subtle, sometimes a little cheeky but always a friend.

Heywood Gina?

Head The wine!

Heywood Oh sorry.

Head Such tenderness, succulent, melting, an unforgettable voyage of exploration for the tongue and mouth.

The choir fades and the Lights come up again

Heywood The chestnut purée?

Head (*Nudging Heywood*) Gina.

Heywood Really?

Head (*wandering out*) I was a young man ... an innocent abroad ... unprepared for the sensual feast that was Italy ... Oh Gina, I remember. Oh Gina, you and the wine and the Tuscan black fish soup.

The Headmaster exits

George What were the names of all those cheese? Did you get them? Mozzarella and what was it?

Tommy Er ... Bill something and er ... Gordon ... er ...

George Gorgonzola. What else? What else?

Tommy Oh, I don't know. Why are you interested in cheese all of a sudden?

George Well I was reading this article in "KERRUNCH", the heavy metal fan's vade-mecum, that said if you eat cheese late at night just before you go to bed you get these really strange dreams. Kind of like, really weird.

Tommy What sort of dreams?

George Well, it was great. Last week I thought I'd try an experiment. I'd tried Cheddar and Cheshire, you know, the basic cheeses and I thought I was ready for something, you know, more kind of, you know, off-beat. So I took the plunge and went straight for the Red Leicester.

Tommy You just don't care, do you?

George No 'cos it was like, you know, important research. So I took the Red Leicester and well it was ... er ... ooooooh!

Tommy Well what did you dream about?

George Oh, I can remember it dead clearly. I was running across this bridge and there were these things chasing me, like, you know, strawberries with legs and these big eyes and you could tell just by looking at these eyes that if they caught you, they'd rip you to bits. They had this really vicious look.

Tommy Vicious strawberries?

George Yes, you could see, like, that it was revenge like for all those years of human beings tearing all those strawberries to pieces, chewing them up and swallowing them. Like the whole Wimbledon bit, you know. And these strawberries wanted to do the same to me.

Tommy Sounds like a nightmare.

George No, it was like beautiful 'cos it was, you know, liberation for fruit, after all these years of oppression, you know, like, Strawberry Power.

Sean (*writing in his diary*) "It appears that the Headmaster is to accompany us on the trip. I think he would be better employed in school. The buildings are in a terrible condition and this would be an ideal time for him to do some painting and decorating."

Heywood Now listen carefully. These are the travel arrangements. We meet at school on Friday at seven-thirty a.m. We travel by coach to Dover ...

Music starts. The chairs are re-arranged to form a coach

SCENE 3

A coach

Music. The following are mimed:

Pupils point out of the windows
Stopping for a boy to be sick
Stopping for driver to be sick
Some fall asleep
The Headmaster points out sights but is ignored
They play with the reclining seats. One boy breaks his and ends up on top of Heywood
They are late and Heywood asks the driver to put his foot down. The coach now rocks violently, lurches round corners finally screeching to a halt. The chairs are re-arranged to resemble the rail of a boat

SCENE 4

A Cross-Channel ferry

The following are mimed:

Drinking in the bar
Playing video games
Throwing objects overboard and at seagulls
Taking photographs
First sight of land
Then there is a storm. The deck tilts madly and they have to walk against heavy winds
They land and convert the set to a train

SCENE 5

A train

The set is converted to resemble a train. The mime conveys that it is very crowded. Occasionally people pass along the corridor with refreshments etc. In one compartment or at one table Heywood is lecturing some bored pupils

Heywood . . . and Napoleon decided that his armies would be able to march better if they had some shade as they travelled these very straight roads which the Romans had built and that's why you see these long straight lines of trees running along each side of the road.

In another part of the train are George, Fordy and John. George is reading a comic

Fordy What you reading, George?

George is engrossed

  George!
George What?

Fordy What are you reading?
George SF.
Fordy Bless you. What are you reading?
George It's amazing. It's called "The Monster That Ate 3B".
John 3B?
Fordy Us?
George Yeah, it's surreal, isn't it? Like 'cos we're 3B and in here, you know, they're 3B and it's, you know . . .
Fordy What's it about?
George I'm just getting to the good bit. This thing from outer space has landed on the school playing field. It's stomped on the caretaker, munched a couple of first years and now it's chasing the headmaster round the art room.
Fordy Monsters!
John How old are you, George?
Fordy Let's read it after you.
John Hey, look. We're beginning to get into the mountains.
George Oh yeah. I know about them. They're the Andes.
Fordy The Alps!
George Well, where are the Andes then?
Fordy ⎫
John ⎭ (*together, deadpan*) On the end of the wristies.

Elsewhere . . .

Frankie Well, what about the war then? How many gears on an Italian tank?
Otto I don't know.

He pulls bar-bells out of his bag. Richie is astonished

Frankie Ten—one forward and nine reverse. (*He laughs*)
Terry Strictly speaking, there's very little truth in these national stereo-types. Over the centuries Italian troops have achieved some of the——
Frankie And what about the food? All grease and garlic.
Otto What are you coming for, if you don't like Italians and you don't like Italian food?
Frankie 'Cos I like Italian women.

The others collapse laughing. Elsewhere . . .

Fletch Look. Look. There's a dog. It's a French dog. That's me first French dog.
Sean (*writing in his journal*) "Fletch has never been abroad before and is very excited."
Fletch Yes, I have! No, I'm not! I was just saying that's all. In case anyone was interested.
Sean "Billy, however, is taking things much more coolly."
Billy Spades are trumps. It's your lead.

Elsewhere . . .

Fordy I'm starving. Have you got anything to eat?
John Just finished me last frog's leg.
Fordy You got anything, George?

No response. He is engrossed in his comic

George!
George What? This is really good. The PE teacher tried to stab this monster with a javelin, only *it* grabbed *him* and now it's like going to eat him like one of them little sausages on sticks.
Fordy Have you got anything to eat?
George Look in me bag.
Fordy Great. (*He starts looking in the bag*) What are you doing with all this cheese? (*He pulls out about eight different French cheeses*)
John I read there are over four hundred French cheeses.
George What? Oh yeah. I bought the ones that looked the most, you know, er . . . mind-blowing.

John and Fordy look at the cheeses with curiosity

Sean (*writing*) "It is eight hours since we departed from Calais and we are now about to leave France. It is hard to sum up in a few short sentences my impressions of this country. As the familiar names passed before me through the window I felt some of the excitement so many travellers have felt before me. Paris—chic, electric, vibrant, bohemian, sophisticated. Burgundy—historic, picturesque, a gastronomic paradise. And the South—ah, the South—sumptuous sunlit days, breathless romantic nights. How could anyone fail to be moved and inspired by the romance and enchantment of this magnificent country?"
Billy Did you shuffle these cards or what?
Head . . . followed by prosciutto, which is ham, Parma ham. They feed the pigs on parsnips to make the meat taste especially sweet. Oh look, we're stopping. Where are we? (*He looks out of the window*) This is it. This is it. This is what I've been waiting for. The first sighting of real Italian ice-cream. Middleton, Middleton come here.

Tommy comes to him

Tommy Sir?
Head Hop off the train over to that café and get me a large bomba.
Tommy A large what?
Head Bomba. Bomba.
Tommy Is it a dance?
Head It's an ice-cream. Hurry up. (*He gives him money*) See if you can get a bottle of Soave.
Tommy After-shave?
Head It's a light white wine. Hurry up.

Tommy mimes getting off the train

Others are looking out. Elsewhere Otto pulls chest expanders out of his bag. Richie looks into the bag

Richie Is this all your luggage? Bar-bells, weights, chest expanders and swimming trunks?
Otto All I need.
Frankie Look at 'em. D'you notice anything?
Otto (*looking*) What d'you mean?
Frankie Look at their faces. What d'you notice?
Otto Suntans.
Frankie Anything else?
Otto No. What?
Frankie No acne. Why do you never see an Italian with spots?
Otto I don't know.
Frankie 'Cos they all slide off. (*He laughs*)
Terry Actually in this hot climate, standards of personal hygiene are generally higher than ours. The idea of the greasy Italian was always largely a myth caused by associating the people with the food they eat which, again with little foundation, was considered to——
Frankie Oh, shut up. It was only a joke.
Richie And what's this?
Otto Will you leave my bag alone!
Richie Baby oil!
Otto Yes. It makes me skin sort of glossy—shows off the muscles to full effect. All the professionals use it. When I get that on I look dead cool and sleek.
Terry Just like an Italian.

They mime the train starting. The Head rushes to the window and shouts

Head Middleton! Middleton! Run, lad!

Heywood rushes to the window

Heywood What's going on?
Head It's Middleton. He went for a bomba.
Heywood Well, why didn't he use the one on the train?
Head It's an ice-cream!

Middleton appears running alongside the train

Be careful, lad!

He leans out and takes the ice-cream and wine. Middleton keeps running

Heywood Of all the . . .

Heywood goes to the door and opens it. He goes down a step and runs with Middleton, grabs him, puts him on the step and gets left behind himself. They all wave as he collapses on the platform. The others mime the train going off

Scene 6

Pericolo di Morte. The town square

Loud Italian music. Suddenly there are shouting Italians everywhere—priests, old women dressed in black, ice-cream sellers, men at street café tables, old men playing dominoes, little children chasing about, mothers hanging out washing across the auditorium etc. etc.

A "mime", all in shouted gibberish Italian, of "typical" Italian street life:

Two men in a café are having a loud argument
A mother tells off a "cool"-looking teenager to the amusement of his friends
The old men and the teenagers exchange abuse
One boy kicks a football, dirtying the washing, which leads to a big chase
Carlo brings drinks out to the men at tables and sits down to join them
Carla emerges from the hotel and hands him the hotel sign to hang up
Carlo does so with a ladder and the shouted encouragement of the men

The Mayor enters pursued by a shouting crowd. He climbs on to a rostrum. He eventually quietens everybody down

Mayor Quiet! Quiet! Silenzio! My friends! We must be calm. We must think. This is a crisis for our town and we must use reason, argument, not hysteria.

They are all calm

   (*Hysterically*) What are we going to do?!

They all erupt again. Eventually one voice is heard over the others

Giuseppe It is the curse of Pericolo!
Mayor Quiet. Quiet.
Giuseppe It is the curse of Pericolo!
Mayor What's that you say, Giuseppe?
Giuseppe It is the curse of Pericolo di Morte!
Mayor Giuseppe, no-one believes that old story any more.

Adults shake their heads

Giuseppe (*cackling*) You would like to forget the curse but it is not so easy. You pretend that it is superstition. You pretend that we no longer believe.
Mayor Giuseppe, we don't have time to listen to your fairy-tales.
Giuseppe The curse is alive today.
Mayor Please, Giuseppe, we must decide——
Giuseppe Ask the children! They know of the curse. They know it is real! (*He grabs a boy*) Tell them. The curse of Pericolo. Tell them the old story that no-one believes.
Boy No, signore. Per favore.
Giuseppe Tell them!
Boy There is the legend of the curse of Pericolo and the sea-beast.

All the townspeople scream involuntarily at the mention of the beast. They then try to turn this into a scornful dismissive laugh. This they do each time the boy mentions the beast

Giuseppe Go on.

Boy They say that it was many hundreds of years ago. The people of Pericolo were very poor, close to starvation. One day a rich merchant was passing through the village ...

Music. The rest of the story is shown in mime:

Two villagers meet the merchant who is displaying his wealth ostentatiously. They become more and more annoyed and greedy at his behaviour. Eventually they attack and murder the merchant. As they remove his jewellery other villagers arrive, are horrified at first, then join in robbing the man. They cart off the body

They threw the body into the sea, knowing that the tides here would carry it far out to sea. It was many months before the next victim stopped in the town ...

In mime the villagers surround and kill him

At first they had been driven by hunger, but soon they were moved only by greed. More and more frequent were their brutal crimes ...

Mime: A series of improvised quickfire comic murders by various means. When they uncover the last body and remove his cloak they shrink back in horror. They have killed a priest

They had killed a priest. On that day, it is said, the black curse fell on Pericolo. On that day came—the sea-beast.

Scream. Laugh

Each day it came to the town to claim new victims. Many were killed. The villagers feared to go near the shore. There could be no more fishing. The town was poorer than ever before. The people prayed for forgiveness. All that they had stolen they gave to the church. Some went on a pilgrimage to Rome. It is said that the curse was then broken. But some say that every hundredth year the sea-beast——

Scream. Laugh

—the sea-beast——

Scream. Laugh

—it returns so that the people of Pericolo shall never forget the crimes of their forefathers.

Giuseppe Do you still tell me that no-one believes in the sea-beast?

Scream. Laugh

Mayor Are you trying to ruin us all?

The crowd erupts

Silenzio! We must forget all about such superstitions. There is no curse of Pericolo di Morte.

Woman What about my little Salvatore? My angel!

Man We don't *know* how he died.
Woman It was the sea-beast——

Scream. Laugh

We all know it was the sea-beast. It has returned and it has taken my Salvatore and the others.

The crowd erupts

Mayor Quiet! All this talk of sea-beasts and curses. This wild talk must stop. It will spread. If it reaches the newspapers there will be no visitors this year. Who will bring his children here to be eaten by a sea-beast?

The Head enters with pupils

Head Excuse me. Per favore, where is the Hotel Calamari? We were expecting to be met at the station . . . stazione.

Carla emerges from the crowd

Carla Benvenuto, signore. Carlo!

Carlo emerges

What is the time?
Carlo Five o'clock, cara mia.
Carla What time are you to meet the train?
Carlo (*guilty*) At four-thirty, cara mia.
Carla (*battering him*) Imbecile. Why did I marry such an imbecile? It is a wonder we have any business at all. If it were left to you, we would be bankrupt. Take the bags.

During the following, Carlo struggles under mountains of the pupils' luggage, taking it into the hotel

I am so sorry, signore. My husband, he is not right in the head. Welcome to Pericolo. (*She shrieks with delight as she looks at the pupils*) What beautiful children! (*She hugs and kisses each one*) Welcome to Italy. Bei ragazzi. Come in. Come in. You must be hungry. I have something very special for you. Come in. Come in.

They are shepherded inside

Woman This is wicked. They must not stay. They must not go near the sea. They will die like my Salvatore. Send them away.
1st Man Don't be a fool. If we send them away we will arouse suspicions.
2nd Man And if one of these English children is killed like the others?
Giuseppe His blood will be on our hands.
Mayor Nobody will be killed. All this talk of killing!
Priest If they stay we must not allow them near the beach. It is too dangerous. We must close the beach to all.
Mayor Father, here we have no ancient monuments, we have no mountains, no volcanoes, no beauty spots. Our visitors come only because we

have the finest beach in the region. If we close the beach they will leave
and no more will come.

2nd Man And will they come when one of these English children is killed?

3rd Man We must take this chance. Three are dead. Perhaps it is over for
this time. Perhaps it has returned to the deep.

2nd Man You cannot take chances with the lives of children.

3rd Man And what of our lives, our children? How will we live if no visitors
come? Last winter was hard—but what of next winter? Will the bank
wait, eh, Roberto, or will you lose your café? When you cannot pay for
your van, Stefano, how will you earn your living? We cannot exist
without the summer tourists.

Mayor Federico is right. We have no choice.

The crowd shouts agreement

Priest Let us pray that we have made the right decision.

All Amen.

They disperse. A mime:

> *The Head and the pupils emerge from the hotel and are seated at tables and
> fed huge quantities of spaghetti and ice-cream. Carla kisses and hugs them
> as she serves. Carlo does a slapstick routine with plates of food*

> *Heywood arrives*

As he approaches the hotel, Giuseppe accosts him to warn him

Giuseppe (*grabbing Heywood*) You must go! Leave at once!

Heywood (*exhausted*) I've only just arrived!

Giuseppe Take the children away from here. The town is cursed.

Heywood What are you talking about? Take your hands off me. Why do the
loonies always pick on me? What's Italian for "take a running jump"?

Giuseppe Listen to me, signore. You must go. If you stay here you will die.
The children will die. The name of this town is death. Go. Do not wait.
Visit Roma or Napoli. They are beautiful cities. Here is nothing for you—
except the beach and in Pericolo di Morte the beach is too close to the
cemetery. (*He cackles bitterly*) Go at once. There is a train in half an hour.
Back to the station.

*He starts to drag Heywood back to the station. Heywood resists. It turns into
a comic tussle. Heywood ends up prone, being dragged towards the station by
his feet, clawing with his hands. Giuseppe has continued talking*

> Venice is very nice at this time of year. And you will love Florence. Go.
> Wherever you go you must not stay here. We don't want you here. Stay
> and you die. You die, signore. You die. The sea-beast. The sea-beast.

The Head notices Heywood and comes across. The struggle continues

Head Heywood, what on earth are you doing?

Heywood I'm enjoying that warm Italian hospitality you were telling me
about. Will you get this madman off me?

Head I say, old chap, signore, amico. Would you mind, my friend has had a very hard day ... Il mio amico ...

Heywood Don't reason with him! Hit him.

Head I don't know whether that would be a very good idea. He might be a godfather.

Heywood What has his family got to do with it? Get him off me!

The Head makes a very tentative effort as Carla arrives

Carla Ey, Giuseppe!

She batters him, screaming in gibberish Italian. He gets up and screams back. They continue for two minutes. The pupils all gather round as do the Italians. At the end Carla and Giuseppe part and everyone applauds enthusiastically. Now the muttered discussions the Italians have been having in pairs become louder and louder. They develop into full-scale rows which continue loudly during ...

Heywood That's all very quaint and interesting but we've all had a long day and it is time we were all in bed.

Fletch What are we doing tomorrow, sir?

Head The first thing I want to do is to get a nice sun-tan. So bright and early tomorrow we'll be off to the beach.

On the word "beach" the Italians all stop arguing simultaneously, turn towards the Head and let out a shriek. A dramatic chord. Black-out. Music as the scene is changed

Scene 7

The beach

Music. The pupils arrive and mime a beach scene. Some throw themselves in the water, swimming, floating on their backs, splashing each other. Others sunbathe. Terry reads an archaeological book. Otto exercises and displays his physique to the nearby girls. Other games. Water-skiing. Other improvised activities

Fletch Look. Look. Look at those girls over there ... and those ... and that one, she's ... and look at her ...

Sean (*writing*) "Fletch has finally discovered girls."

Fletch No, I haven't. I mean, I discovered them months ago ... years ... I've always known about them.

Billy Do you think they'd know how to play pontoon?

Heywood and the Head arrive. The Head has a twelve-inch high multi-coloured drink in his hand and a huge picnic basket. Heywood is in huge flowery shorts

Head Oh stop worrying, Heywood. It was a perfectly natural mistake. He looked far too old to be her husband.

Heywood What if he's in the Mafia? He was furious. There's probably a contract out on us right now. (*He looks around nervously*)
Head What a beauty, eh Heywood?
Heywood She was at least sixty-five years old!
Head Not her! This! Campari and champagne.

He slurps it noisily. Elsewhere Otto exercises while Tommy watches

Tommy Where are they then?
Otto Eh?
Tommy Where are they?
Otto Where are what?
Tommy You said, "When those Italian girls see me magnificent physique, they'll be all over me."
Otto They will. Give them a chance.
Tommy Give them a chance? You've been at that for half an hour. The only ones that have looked at you are those two over there.
Otto Where? Do you think they fancy me? Which ones?
Tommy They certainly find you entertaining. They haven't stopped laughing for ten minutes.
Otto That's good. It's a good start to get them laughing. Where are they? I'll go over there, very casually of course, and give them a close-up of my rippling muscles.
Tommy There.

He points, laughing. Otto's face falls

What's the matter?
Otto They're nuns!
Tommy Well, so what? Some of those nuns have got very dirty habits.

Tommy screams with laughter. Otto continues to exercise

Heywood Look at those boys! (*He shouts*) Webster, Tourneur, come here!

They do

Look at you!

They try to

Chasing about in this sun without any protection.
Cyril It's all right, sir. I can look after meself, sir. I do karate.
Heywood No. Protection from the sun. Haven't you got any suntan lotion?
John I don't need any, sir. I tan naturally.
Cyril Yes, sir. So do I. I never burn, sir.
Heywood This is not Blackpool, Webster. This is southern Italy. The sun is fierce. Look at the temperature now and it's only early yet. Tourneur, I think I can see your shoulders turning red already.

The Head opens his picnic basket and starts to assemble a salad

Cyril I don't think so, sir.
Heywood You had better go and buy some.

John But it's really expensive here, sir.

Heywood Well, you should have thought of that before you came away, shouldn't you?

Cyril Oh, sir!

Heywood Actually, you can use this. (*He produces a bottle of olive oil*) Olive oil. It's cheaper than lotion and works quite well.

The Head sees the oil, takes it and pours it on his lettuce

For very strong sun like this I always use a concoction an aunt of mine used to make up. Here. Look. (*He brings out a tub of creamy substance*) It's made from powdered chalk, believe it or not, with some white of egg, glycerine and furniture polish.

The Head sees it, takes it, puts a large spoonful on to his salad and starts to eat

(*Staring in horror*) Well, boys, if you're in agony with sunburn tomorrow, don't expect me to look after you. Go on.

They go. Heywood takes off his shirt and reaches for the lotion. The Head gets there first and helps himself to another huge dollop. George has joined Tommy and Otto, who is still exercising

A group of Italian boys appears. They all look very "cool". They strut. Comb their hair. Pose themselves elegantly. Frankie wolf-whistles. The Italians glare, mutter together and sneer. The word "Inglesi" is followed by spitting

Frankie Did you hear that ?"Englishy" means "English", doesn't it Terry?

Terry "Inglesi" actually. Yes, "English".

Frankie Who do they think they're spitting at? (*He starts to get up aggressively*)

Terry Sit down. Serves you right for whistling at them.

Frankie Well, they'd just better watch out, insulting us.

Sean (*writing*) "I am pleased to see that common sense and a cordial spirit of European comradeship have triumphed over the baser aggressive and territorial instincts which were apparent amongst the less mature members of the group."

Frankie produces a little Union Jack and sticks it in the sand. The Italians jabber in gibberish and then produce an Italian flag. Luigi has to be restrained from tackling the English group. The Italians prepare to go swimming

Just as they are about to do so, their enormous mothers appear and shriek at them not to go near the water, miming the sea-beast's attacks. The mothers exit

The English find this very funny. The Italians play football instead

Fletch appears carrying three ice-creams with difficulty

An Italian playing football bumps him and one ice-cream accidentally goes in the Italian's face. He turns to Fletch, takes the second ice-cream and pushes it in Fletch's face, then takes the third and puts it in Fletch's swimming trunks.

Fletch waddles across to the English boys who react as might be expected and the two sides square up to each other. A fight is about to start when Heywood notices and shouts

Heywood Beaumont, Otway, Middleton, Webster! Stop it at once. (*He separates them*) You are supposed to be here to promote harmony and understanding between our two nations, not to start brawling on the beach like a bunch of mods and rockers.
Head (*finishing his picnic*) It's time for lunch. Everybody back to the hotel. Come along.

He and Heywood go . . .

Leaving the two sets of boys staring fiercely at each other

Frankie Terry!
Terry What?
Frankie Tell them we'll meet them here tonight.
Otto Midnight.
Heywood (*off*) Rattigan!
Frankie If they don't turn up, we'll know it's true that all Italians are cowards.

Terry translates this

Heywood (*off*) Beaumont! Middleton! Come along. Right now.

The English leave

The Italians jeer after them

Their mothers then appear and clip them round the ears

SCENE 8

The beach—midnight

The beach is lit by a string of bulbs on poles which flash on and off at times accompanied by electrical fizzes and crackles

The Mayor, Giuseppe and Carlo enter separately and stand looking out to sea. Romantic music. They see and greet each other

Mayor Buona sera, Giuseppe, Carlo. Business is good, eh Carlo?
Carlo Si si. I am very busy but is very good. I like to walk here on the beach when all the guests have gone to bed. It is the only peaceful part of the day for me.

The lights flicker and crackle. They turn to look at them

Mayor They should be replaced. Perhaps this year if we have a good season.
Giuseppe He is out of there, waiting.
Carlo (*nervously*) Oh Giuseppe, please don't.

Mayor Don't tell me YOU believe his nonsense?
Carlo No no, of course not ... but sometimes, when I walk here alone at night I feel ... I feel ...
Mayor What?
Carlo I feel as if someone or something is watching me.
Mayor (*looking at the audience*) Ridiculous.
Giuseppe No, I feel it too. He is watching us now.

The lights flicker, go out, crackle, come on again as Carlo shrieks and then looks embarrassed

Carlo It is time I was going back. I have still the washing up to do.
Giuseppe You are wise, Carlo. It is not good to stay here. Are you coming, Signor Mayor?
Mayor (*slightly worried*) No! You are grown men. How can you be so foolish?
Carlo (*going with Giuseppe*) Buona notte, signore.
Giuseppe (*to the water*) Buona notte.

They go

Mayor (*shouting after them*) We are civilized men. We have no monsters! (*He looks out to sea*) Something watching. Huh. They have the hearts of mice, not of men. Where would we be if we followed such as they? Man cannot be ruled by fear.

Sinister music. Splashing noises, growing louder

We must forget these legends, these superstitions. (*He is looking nervous. He shouts out to sea*) There are no sea-monsters!

The lights flicker and go out. Monster noises. The Mayor screams. When the lights come on again he has gone

A clock strikes midnight. Frankie enters, pushing Terry

Terry I don't want anything to do with this.
Frankie We need you to translate in case they start insulting us again.
Terry You've just come to have a fight.
Frankie Well we need you for that too.
Terry I won't be doing any fighting. I shall do my best to restore peace. We are supposed to be here in friendship.

The other English boys arrive

John Are they here yet?
Terry They've probably got more sense.
Frankie They may be further down the beach. Come on.

They go. Terry tries to go the other way but Frankie intercepts him and pushes him ahead

Luigi and Eduardo enter

Eduardo They are guests in our country. We should not fight them.

Luigi They have challenged us. They will call us cowards if we do not. Already we have this reputation with the English. Have you not heard it? Tonight we will show them they are wrong.

Eduardo We also have another reputation. We are hospitable. We are friendly. We are warm and welcoming. What of that?

Luigi We will give them a very warm welcome. I hope.

Other Italians arrive

Will we not, amici miei?

They agree heartily

Dario It is after midnight. Where are they?

The English appear at the other side

The two groups see each other and with a yell approach each other. Eduardo and Terry shout and hold up their own sides

Terry Please let me try to make peace.

Frankie You're wasting your time but go ahead.

Eduardo has the same conversation with Luigi in mime. Terry and Eduardo meet in the middle

Eduardo Buona notte.

Terry Buona notte.

They shake hands

Eduardo I speak a little English.

Terry Oh good ... erm ... look ... there is no need for us to fight.

Eduardo Si. No need. But my friends say that you challenge us. It would be a dishwasher not to accept.

Terry A *dishonour*. Yes, I see, my friends are upset about the ice-cream. Perhaps, if your friend would apologize about the ice-cream.

Eduardo I will ask him.

Eduardo approaches the boy who is looking extremely vicious, brandishing a weapon, having to be held back. Eduardo takes one look and returns to Terry without speaking to the boy

I don't think he will.

Terry Well he started it. Are you sure you couldn't persuade him?

Eduardo (*looking at the boy*) No, he is imperishable.

Terry *Implacable*, yes. No possibility of compromise?

Eduardo It is a matter of honour for him.

Terry And for us.

Eduardo Well we have tried to keep the peas.

Terry *Peace*, yes. And they won't listen to reason.

Both So ...

Terry and Eduardo attack each other vigorously. Music. The two groups move forwards. Both groups have weapons—beach umbrellas etc. The lights fizz and go out. Music. The lights go on and off intermittently revealing a pitched battle taking place all over the auditorium. Finally the house lights go on to show all exhausted, collapsed or unconscious. The unconscious are carried out

ACT II

The beach. Dawn

Music. The following is mimed:

> *It is dawn. An Italian is cleaning up the beach, putting out chairs etc. He picks up various bits of rubbish and puts them in his sack. He comes across the Mayor's head and puts that in too. Double-take. Horror. He takes out the head, drops it, runs off, runs back, puts the head on a table, runs off. He returns with a Policeman and a Priest. He shows them the head. The Priest gives it the last rites. The Policeman interviews the Cleaner who re-enacts in mime how he found the head. The Policeman is writing all this down with the Priest correcting the spellings. The Policeman has to keep tearing off a page and starting again*

> *Unseen by the others, the Head enters exercising and taking deep breaths. He then sits at the table where the Mayor's head is but he doesn't see it as he is concentrating on assembling his breakfast*

The Italians notice him and grab the head just as he turns. The Policeman holds it behind his back. The Headmaster holds out his hand to shake hands with the Policeman. The Policeman signals to the Cleaner who takes the head. The Headmaster then comes to the Cleaner to shake hands and offers him a croissant. The Cleaner throws the head to the Priest who catches it. But the Headmaster is making his way to the Priest to shake his hand and give him a croissant. The Headmaster is between the Priest and the others. The Priest quickly points out to sea and behind the Headmaster's back bounces the head across to the Policeman who catches it in a box and slams the lid on it. (The head is a disguised ball and bounces very well.) The Headmaster continues his breakfast

The Italians go

Heywood enters in agony. He is sunburnt all over. He sits very gingerly

Heywood Aaaaagh!
Head Sunburnt.
Heywood Just a touch. (*He leans back in his seat and screams with pain*)
Head What about your aunt's special suntan recipe?
Heywood You tell *me*. You ate most of it. There's only one consolation. Those lads will be sorry they didn't listen to me. If I'm red raw with all that oil on, what sort of state will be they be in this morning? I bet they didn't get much sleep last night. They'll be like beetroots.

Music starts. The boys enter. They have all developed rich tans

Head Look more like walnuts to me.

Heywood Goldsmith, come here. (*He stands and examines his tan*) It's not possible. You got this out of a bottle, didn't you?

Two boys are playing with a beach ball. It hits Heywood in the middle of his back. He leaps in the air with a shriek of pain. He chases the boy around. The Head stuffs himself with food as the music continues. Mimed beach activities. Luigi is swimming. Frankie floats out to sea on an air-bed

The Policeman prowls, looking out for the sea-monster

Heywood This sun. It's fierce. (*He wriggles uncomfortably*)

Head Just think of the wine we could make if we had weather like this in England.

Olly Everyone'll be dead jealous when I get back with this bronzy.

Heywood (*jealous*) Goldsmith, get your clothes on. I want you to go into town for me.

Olly Oh, sir!

Heywood Mr Russell asked me to bring him back a "Specchio".

Olly But sir, I was trying to build up a good tan.

Heywood Stop moaning, lad. Look, it's clouding over anyway.

It grows darker

Looks like we might have a shower.

Thunderclap. Downpour

Here. Quickly. (*He gives him money*)

Olly What was it you wanted?

Heywood A "Specchio". It's a news magazine. Here I'll write it down. Hurry up.

They all grab their things and run off except for Olly

SCENE 2

Around the town

Music. The following is mimed: In the newsagent's two Italian boys are browsing, looking at a dirty magazine. Olly finds his "Specchio", buys it. The Italians run off with the dirty mag. The owner gives chase. He meets a Policeman, indicates the boys. The Policeman chases. Olly watches the chase which goes all around the auditorium, across the audience and out of the door. The boys run on to the stage behind him and bump into him. They plant the stolen mag on him and run off. The Policeman puffs on. He rests, sees Olly who has bought an ice-cream and is about to eat it on a bench. He pulls out the magazine to look at. It is the dirty one. The Policeman sees it. Olly tries to explain. Decides to run for it. The Policeman pursues him. Through streets, around corners. He grabs dark glasses and a big hat to cover his face. He tries hiding in a cinema. Clambers over people to a vacant seat. Has to keep moving seats to avoid the Policeman. Gets involved watching the film. Later in the chase they burst into a church, realize where they are, slow down, make the sign of cross, holy water, tiptoe out, then back to sprint. Olly runs on to the beach, sees a snorkel lying there, puts it on and hides underwater. The Policeman arrives, sees the snorkel top, grabs it, pushes it under water. Olly surfaces, squirts mouthful of water at the Policeman, escapes. Olly, passing a shop, grabs a skirt and girl's hat and puts them on. Runs into a bar. Sits next to an Italian Youth. He sees "her". Starts to chat her up. Offers her a drink. Olly is irritated but as the Policeman enters he accepts and smiles at the Youth. The Policeman looks around suspiciously and watches them. The Youth invites Olly to come back to his place. Olly refuses, then looks at the Policeman approaching, looks at the Youth, looks at the audience, puts his arm round the Youth's waist and goes out with him past the Policeman

Scene 3

At sea, near a rock

Frankie is floating on his air-bed, asleep. Luigi is on the rock

Luigi Aiuto! Aiuto!

Frankie stirs, sits up, looks around, panics

Frankie What? What happened to the sun? What happened to the beach? Oh no. (*Very phoney*) I should have listened to the warnings. You should never go to sleep on an air-bed in the sea. Winds and tides can easily carry you into danger. Always take care with air-beds.

Luigi Aiuto!

Frankie Aiuto? (*He pulls a phrase book out of his swimming trunks and looks it up*) Aiuto ... aiuto ... Help.

Luigi Aiuto!

Frankie Help?

He looks, sees Luigi, paddles over. Luigi clambers on to the bed, almost sinking them both

Luigi Grazie.

Frankie You could have drowned there ... if I hadn't been here. You should never swim out of your depth you know. And you've got to watch out for the tides. They can carry you miles out before you know it. And the weather can change very quickly round here. One minute bright and sunny. Next moment a thunderstorm.

Suddenly the sky brightens

There you are, you see. Sun's out again. Just like that.

Luigi (*recovering*) It is hard to understand you. Your accent ...

Frankie What? I don't understand Italian.

The air-bed is sinking

Luigi The bed is sinking!
Frankie The bed won't hold us both!
Luigi There is a rock over there.
Frankie Look. There's a rock over there.
Luigi The rock.
Frankie Rock. Rock. What the hell's the Italian for rock? Rocko!
Luigi No, Luigi. How do you do?

They shake hands

Frankie No. Paddle the bed towards that rock.
Luigi We must try to reach that rock.

They paddle to the rock and climb on. The bed collapses

Frankie Well that bed won't get us back. Looks like we're stuck. Not much room here. I wonder if the tide gets any higher than this. (*He decides to mime this to Luigi*) Does the tide ... the water ... the tide ... get any higher ... higher ... over the rock?
Luigi Yes.
Frankie That means "Yes". Oh no. How high? How ... high? (*He holds his hand about one foot above the rock*) This high. Water up to here? (*Two feet*) Here? (*Three feet*) This high?

Luigi stands up and holds his hand well above his head

Luigi High tide is in three hours.

Frankie gulps. Luigi sits. Pause

Frankie Could we swim back?

He mimes it. All the following is mimed (only?)

Luigi I am a strong swimmer. I might make it but what about you?
Frankie No. I am a very poor swimmer. You could go and bring help.
Luigi It would take too long. You would drown before I got back.
Frankie You go. Save yourself.
Luigi (*thinking about it*) I will stay with you. Perhaps a boat will pass.
Frankie The storm will have made everyone go indoors.

Pause

   I wish I'd learnt to speak a bit of Italian.
Luigi You have saved my life for nothing, I think. The water is rising.

Pause

Frankie Drowning. I never thought of drowning. I always thought I'd live to be ninety. I'll never know what was going to happen in my life. I was just getting to the best part too. Just beginning to get interesting. (*After a pause*) Please. You should go. You could get back. No point in us both drowning.

Luigi I do not understand you.

Frankie You understand me all right. Go.

Luigi (*in English, with an accent*) You think we Italians are cowards. Well, this is one Italian who is not.

Frankie Hey, I thought you didn't speak English!

Luigi We are in Italy. Always you English expect everyone to speak *your* language.

Frankie If Terry was here, I'd be all right. He speaks Italian very well. I couldn't be bothered. I suppose I wasn't interested in speaking to you.

Luigi It is difficult to talk to each other, I think.

Frankie Listen, you should go. There's no point in you staying if you're a strong swimmer.

Luigi I have said, "No". I will stay with you. My arm, she is injured last night. The fight. That is why I needed help. Usually I swim much further than this.

Frankie Yes, I expect there are quite a few bruised Eyetie . . . Italians on the beach today.

Luigi On the beach, yes. The English are in the hospital I think.

Frankie Oh, come on. We destroyed you.

Luigi Madre mia, your English . . . er . . . arroganza? . . . it makes me sick.

Frankie Arrogance? Make you sick, do I? Well why don't you just go? You don't think I'm enjoying your company, do you? Go on. Get in there. Wash some of the grease off.

Luigi OK, you said it. I will go.

Frankie What are you waiting for?

Luigi OK. OK. OK. OK.

He dives in and swims away

Frankie Send help! I'll stay afloat as long as I can.

Frankie wanders around the rock trying to measure the size of it. Then does it again to see if it has got smaller. It has

The sea-monster appears and attacks him. He struggles but is being dragged under when Luigi appears and rescues him, frightening the monster off. They are on the rock again

You saved my life there.

Luigi That makes us even.

Frankie Do you think it will come back?

Luigi I cannot tell.

Frankie Are you going to try swimming back again?

Luigi If I leave you alone and the monster she return, you could not fight her off alone.

Frankie Yeah. And if you were swimming back and it came after you . . .

Luigi Si. We must stay together I think.

Frankie It can't kill the two of us.

Luigi I hope.

Music. They look at each other. Smile. shake hands

SCENE 4

The town square

Music. Heywood, the Head and the boys are dozing in the sun outside the hotel. The Goldonis bring out drinks. A chorus of snores. One boy is trying to get to sleep but has to keep moving to avoid noisy neighbours. Flies are troublesome. John is ordering all sorts of drinks and getting very drunk. Billy and Fletch are playing cards. Sean writes in his journal

Sean "Anglo-Italian relations are at a low ebb. Most of us are nursing minor injuries after last night's battle on the beach. Heywood and the Head are asleep again. Alcoholism is a terrible thing. I now realize that foreign travel is the only way really to understand the people of other lands. However much you may read or see on television about Italy, it is only when you are here surrounded by Italian life and Italian culture that you begin to understand the complications and subtleties of the Italian character. The sheer force and impact of Italy on the traveller are overwhelming."

Billy (*laying down cards*) A royal flush! Have you any idea of the odds against that?

A mob of Italians arrives. They are screaming and shouting at each other. The Policeman occasionally pulls the Mayor's head out of the box and puts it back. A great uproar

The English are all awoken

Head Go and see what's going on, Heywood. This is supposed to be siesta time.

Heywood Webster!

John Yeshir.

John totters over to the mob who rave on. He sees the Mayor's head displayed and totters back

Heywood Well?

John It's a head, sir.

Heywood What's ahead?

Head It's behind, you stupid boy.

Heywood What are you talking about, Webster? Ford!

Fordy Sir?

Heywood What is all that fuss about?

Fordy (*looking*) It's the head, sir.

Head Me? It certainly is not.

Heywood Oh I suppose I'll have to go and see. (*He gets up*)

Fordy It is a head, sir. The policeman's got one in that box.

Heywood Ford, you have a regrettably sick sense of humour.

John No shir, it ish shir. It's a head.

Heywood gives John a suspicious look and goes over to the crowd

Heywood Excuse me! Per favore!

The crowd notice him, freeze and go silent

We were trying to have a little siesta ... you see ... one of your Italian customs I understand ... when in Rome ...

The crowd look at each other muttering "Roma?" and shaking their heads ...

and it was a little noisy.

Fordy Ask him about the head, sir.

Heywood What about him?

Fordy No, sir. There's a head in that box, sir.

He points. The Italians react

Heywood What's the matter? You don't mean to tell me that what this boy says is true ... May I ...?

Frankie, Luigi and a fisherman enter

Frankie Sir, sir, it's all right. Don't worry. I'm quite safe.

Heywood Be quiet, Beaumont. I want to see in——

Frankie I'm sorry if you've been looking for me but——

Heywood Looking for you?

Luigi and the fisherman are miming their rescue. Passing, he saw them on the rock and picked them up. Luigi mimes what happened in Scene 3

Frankie You haven't been looking for me?

Heywood What on earth do you mean?

Frankie (*hurt*) I've been missing for hours! I floated out on my air-bed and it deflated and Luigi and I were stranded on this rock and the tide was coming in and then we were attacked by a huge monster.

As he says "monster", Luigi reaches the word "mostro" in his story. The Italians gasp. The English sit bolt upright. Panic breaks out. Everyone runs about madly. Suddenly they stop. Terry and Eduardo are arguing, building up to a fight. The other English and Italian boys talk in a friendly way

Head (*to Frankie*) And how long were the two of you there?

Frankie Hours.

Policeman And what's this about a fight on the beach last night?

Luigi It is true. It was foolish. Now the English and Italians are friends.

Olly, still in girl's clothes runs on, pursued by the amorous Youth

Olly Sir, sir.

Head Goldsmith! Why are you wearing those clothes?

Olly Oh, sir. Help me, please. Will you get rid of this feller?!

Youth Il tuo padre? Signore ... (*He takes the Head to one side*)

Olly Oh, sir, it's been a nightmare!

Heywood Well, why dress up as a girl?

Olly I had to disguise myself to get away from the police.

Heywood What? Why were the police after you, for goodness sake?

Olly That was because of the porno magazine and the shoplifting.

The Head and the Youth come forward

Oh, sir, have you explained I'm a boy?

Head As far as I can understand he's just asked me for your hand in marriage.

Olly Sir, tell him to get lost!

Head His family seem to be very well off. I should give the idea some consideration.

Olly Sir!

Youth Cara mia. (*He pursues Olly round the Head and Heywood*)

Heywood Goldsmith, did you get my magazine?

Olly gives him the dirty one

Goldsmith! This is pornographic.

Head Surely not. Let me see. (*He looks at it with interest*)

Olly Look!

He removes the skirt and hat and gives back the rose the Youth gave him. The Youth holds the rose, sadly turns away from Olly, walks over, sees Terry still arguing, smiles, offers the rose to him. Terry batters him. Eduardo joins in on the Youth's side. A fight starts. Luigi and Frankie break it up

Head (*ham*) Never mind all that. There's a monster on the loose out there and I want to know what you're going to do about it.

Policeman It's all right, signore. I have a plan.

Heywood Well, let's hear it.

Policeman Everybody will have to help.

Heywood Yes, but what is the plan?

Policeman Well we lure the monster on to the beach by the rocks, having first stretched nets between the rocks underwater. When the monster is in the shallow water we pull in the nets, drag the monster ashore and kill it. It will take all the manpower we have—your boys also.

Head Now just a minute . . .

The English boys are all very keen and shout "Yeee-es", "Go on, sir", "I've never killed a monster"

Heywood Ridiculous. This monster is not going to appear with the entire population crawling all over the rocks and beach.

Policeman Ah, no, no, signore. You do not understand. Everybody will be congealed . . .

Heywood Concealed.

Policeman Ah, si. We will be concealed. The bait will appear to be all alone on the beach.

Head The bait?

Policeman I think one of the children would be best. It is very fond of children.

Tommy is still relishing the prospect of monster-bashing, miming how he will finish it off. Everyone looks at him. He notices. Stops

Tommy What's up?

Heywood and the Policeman pick him up and carry him off

Heywood Nothing to worry about, Middleton. There's hardly any chance at all that you'll be killed.

They exit

SCENE 5

The beach

Music. Heywood leads/pushes Tommy into position. The others have all disappeared

Tommy Sir, I know you hate me, sir, but feeding me to a monster is a bit much, sir.
Heywood Don't be silly, Middleton. Nobody's feeding you to a monster. All you have to do is to stand here and look tempting.

Tommy attempts to look seductive

Not like that. Look ... well try to look tasty.
Tommy I don't want to look tasty. You're killing me, sir. It's very unprofessional you know, sir, for a teacher to kill one of his pupils.
Heywood What are you worrying about? As soon as this monster appears we'll all leap out from our hiding places and wipe it out.
Tommy They've all gone!
Heywood No. They're just hiding. Look. Everybody! Just show yourselves for a moment to reassure our bait here, will you?

No one appears

Yoo hoo! Everybody! Let's just see you for a moment, can we?
Tommy (*wailing*) Sir! Please, sir! I promise, sir, next time we have a test I'll get full marks. It's not fair to kill me because I can't remember who won the Hundred Years War!
Heywood Oh stop it. They're only teasing you. Now I'll be just behind this rock.
Tommy Oh sir!
Heywood Middleton, pull yourself together. Get in the water.
Tommy I'm too young to die!
Heywood Further into the water, Middleton.

As he steps further in, the monster appears

George enters

George (*seeing the monster*) Oh wow! This Gorgonzola is amazing!

A Titanic struggle. The monster is winning and has Tommy in its clutches. Heywood runs up and down in a panic shouting

Heywood OK everybody. It's here. Don't panic, Middleton. Just hold on. Everbody! The monster!

Then Otto appears and aims a karate chop at the monster. It has no effect and he chops it again. This fails. He pulls a gun from his pocket and shoots it dead. It is brought ashore. Nervous heads now appear at all entrances and everyone creeps on. They all tentatively examine the dead monster

Well done, Otway, Middleton! You're heroes. They'll probably put your statues in the town square.

Tommy Oh, it was nothing really. When the call came I was ready!

Carla rushes on, grabs Tommy, hugs him and smothers him in kisses. He is lifted on to the shoulders of the Italians

Head Jolly good show, Heywood. Could we have a photograph of this thing do you think? I'd rather like to send it to the local paper ... and I forgot to let them know how we thrashed the King's School First Eleven last week. They're an independent school, you know. Quite a feather in our caps ...

Heywood Yes. Listen everybody. Signori, signore. Could we have a photograph ... photo ... All gather round the monster please.

They all do, English and Italian intermingled. Frankie and George remain to one side

Frankie This is all like that comic of yours. The monster that ate 3B. It nearly did.

George (*stepping to the front and adopting on oratorical pose*) Yes, Frankie, we have like, er ... defeated, you know, the monster of Pericolo di Morte. And why?

Frankie Because it was eating people!

Terry No, Frankie, because it stopped being a secret, because the people of Pericolo faced up to it. And there's a lesson there for all of us, isn't there, Frankie?

Frankie (*astonished*) Is there?

Head We all have our monsters, Frankie.

Frankie Me brother, you mean?

Tommy No, Frankie, we all have our monsters—here, in our hearts. And it is only by facing up to them that they can be defeated.

The others are all waiting for the photograph. Heywood has walked up behind Tommy and Frankie. He listens in disbelief

Heywood What a load of drivel! Will you two get over there!

He beats them over to the group. Music. Flash of camera. Freeze. The Lights fade on group but a spot on the sea area reveals a miniature baby version of the monster which cries, "Mama, Mama." The Lights fade on this too

CURTAIN

FURNITURE AND PROPERTY LIST

Only basic props are listed here—see Production Notes

ACT I

SCENE 1

On stage: Sea, sand, rocks
Fishing rod for **Italian Boy**

Off stage: "ITALY" sign **(Stagehand)**
During black-out on page 1, replace "ITALY" sign with one with huge bite out of it

SCENE 2

On stage: Desks, chairs
Mug of coffee on **Heywood**'s desk

Personal: **George:** personal stereo playing heavy metal music
Heywood: list
Pupils: various forms—see text pages 3-4
Sean: notebook, pen (required throughout)

SCENE 3

On stage: Chairs arranged as coach

SCENE 4

On stage: Chairs arranged as boat-rail

SCENE 5

On stage: Chairs and tables arranged as train
Comic for **George**
Bag containing bar-bells, chest expanders, swimming trunks, baby oil for **Otto**
Playing cards for **Billy**
Bag containing different cheeses
Other luggage

Off stage: Ice-cream, bottle of wine **(Tommy)**

Personal: **Headmaster:** money

SCENE 6

On stage: Rostrum
Chairs and tables arranged as street café
Dominoes on table
Washing for **Mothers** to hang out
Football for **Boy**

Off stage: Drinks **(Carlo)**
Hotel sign **(Carla)**
Ladder **(Carlo)**
Luggage **(Head, Pupils)**
Plates of spaghetti, ice-cream **(Carlo, Carla)**

Personal: **Merchant:** jewellery

SCENE 7

On stage: Sea, sand, rocks
Tables, chairs
Beach equipment and games
Archaeological book for **Terry**

Off stage: Drink, picnic basket containing salad ingredients, plate, spoon, fork
(Head)
Bag with olive oil, tub of cream **(Heywood)**
Football **(Italian Boys)**
3 ice-creams **(Fletch)**

Personal: **Italian Boys:** combs, small Italian flag
Frankie: small Union Jack

SCENE 8

On stage: As Scene 7, plus:
String of flashing bulbs on poles
Chairs, tables folded up

Off stage: Weapons (beach umbrellas etc.) **(Italian** and **English Boys)**

ACT II

SCENE 1

On stage: As Scene 8, plus:
Rubbish
Mayor's "head"
Sack for **Cleaner**
Box

Off stage: Breakfast items **(Head)**
Air-bed **(Frankie)**
Beach ball **(Boys)**

SCENE 2

The following props are used during the mime on pages 23-24
Dirty magazine (**Italian Boys,** then **Olly**)
"Specchio" magazine **(Olly)**
Ice-cream **(Olly)**
Dark glasses, big hat **(Olly)**
Snorkel **(Olly)**
Skirt, girl's hat **(Olly)**

SCENE 3

On stage: Rock, sea
Air-bed for **Frankie**

Personal: **Frankie:** phrase-book in pocket

SCENE 4

On stage: Chairs, tables arranged outside hotel as Scene 6
Cards for **Billy** and **Fletch**

Off stage: Drinks **(Carlo, Carla)**
Box with head **(Policeman)**
Dirty magazine, rose **(Olly)**

SCENE 5

On stage: Sea, sand, rocks
Tables, chairs, beach equipment as Scene 7

Personal: **Otto:** gun

LIGHTING PLOT

Property fittings required: string of flashing bulbs on beach

Various simple exterior and interior settings

ACT I

To open: Moonlight

Cue 1	**Italian Boy** (*singing*): "Campanile." *Fade moonlight to black-out*	(Page 1)
Cue 2	After screams and horrifying noises *Bring up moonlight again*	(Page 1)
Cue 3	When ready for Scene 2 *Lighting on classroom*	(Page 2)
Cue 4	**Head:** ". . . a Riserva Chianti and——" *Fade to pink spot on* **Head**	(Page 5)
Cue 5	**Head:** ". . . tongue and mouth." *Return to previous lighting*	(Page 5)
Cue 6	When ready for Scene 3 *Lighting on coach*	(Page 7)
Cue 7	When ready for Scene 4 *Lighting on cross-Channel ferry*	(Page 7)
Cue 8	When ready for Scene 5 *Lighting on train*	(Page 7)
Cue 9	When ready for Scene 6 *Sunny lighting on town square*	(Page 11)
Cue 10	Dramatic chord *Black-out*	(Page 15)
Cue 11	When ready for Scene 7 *Sunny lighting on beach*	(Page 15)
Cue 12	When ready for Scene 8 *Night lighting on beach; string of bulbs flashing on and off at times*	(Page 18)
Cue 13	**Carlo:** ". . . the day for me." *Lights flicker*	(Page 18)
Cue 14	**Giuseppe:** ". . . watching us now." *Lights flicker, go out, then come on again*	(Page 19)
Cue 15	**Mayor:** " . . . no sea-monsters!" *Lights flicker and go out*	(Page 19)

Cue 16	When ready	(Page 19)
	Bring up lights again	
Cue 17	During fight	(Page 21)
	Lights go on and off intermittently	
Cue 18	At end of fight	(Page 21)
	Bring up house lights	

ACT II

To open: Dawn lighting on beach

Cue 19	**Heywood** enters in agony	(Page 22)
	Increase to sunny lighting	
Cue 20	**Heywood:** "... it's clouding over anyway."	(Page 23)
	Fade lighting	
Cue 21	When ready for Scene 2	(Page 23)
	General lighting around town	
Cue 22	When ready for Scene 3	(Page 24)
	Dull lighting on sea	
Cue 23	**Frankie:** "Next moment a thunderstorm"	(Page 24)
	Increase to sunny lighting	
Cue 24	When ready for Scene 4	(Page 27)
	Sunny lighting on town square	
Cue 25	When ready for Scene 5	(Page 30)
	Sunny lighting on beach	
Cue 26	The group freezes	(Page 31)
	Fade lights on group; bring up spot on baby monster in sea	
Cue 27	Baby monster cries "Mama, Mama"	(Page 31)
	Fade spot to black-out	

EFFECTS PLOT

ACT I

Cue 17	**Mayor:** "... be ruled by fear." *Sinister music, splashing noises, growing louder*	(Page 19)
Cue 18	Lights flicker and go out *Monster noises*	(Page 19)
Cue 19	Lights come up again *Clock strikes midnight*	(Page 19)
Cue 20	During fight *Music; fizzes and crackles as lights go on and off*	(Page 21)

ACT II

Cue 21	As Scene 1 opens *Music for mime*	(Page 22)
Cue 22	**Heywood:** "... be like beetroots." *Music*	(Page 23)
Cue 23	**Heywood:** "... might have a shower." *Thunderclap, downpour of rain—fade when ready for Scene 2*	(Page 23)
Cue 24	During Scene 2 *Music for mimes*	(Page 23)
Cue 25	As monster attacks **Frankie** *Monster noises*	(Page 26)
Cue 26	**Luigi:** "I hope." *Music—continue as Scene 4 opens*	(Page 26)
Cue 27	As Scene 5 opens *Music*	(Page 30)
Cue 28	Monster appears *Monster noises*	(Page 30)
Cue 29	As **Otto** shoots monster *Gunshot*	(Page 31)
Cue 30	**Heywood** beats **Tommy** and **Frankie** over to group *Music, flash of camera*	(Page 31)